This anthology is dedicated to
James Conway,
founder and chairperson of
Rathmines Writers' Workshop,
with thanks for his long standing
commitment of twenty nine years.

Acknowledgments

Thanks are due to –
Gerry O'Donnell for the cover image and design.
Brendan Devlin for collecting submissions and introducing group to the 21st century and Google Drive.
Christine Broe and Liam McNevin for layout.
Mary Guckian, whose years of experience of publishing kept us all on track.
Proof readers – Eithne Cavanagh, James Conway,
Mary Guckian, Anne O'Neill and eagle eyed Susan Flynn.

Beneath the Clock

New Writing
by
Rathmines Writers' Workshop

Edited by Ger Reidy

Swan Press

Published 2019
Swan Press
32 Joy Street
Dublin 4

Copyright Swan Press and individual authors, 2019

ISBN   978-0-9933415-4-0

Cover image and design by Gerry O'Donnell.

Printed by Lia Media,
Phone: 087 2429 586
liamedia15@gmail.com

Foreword

When James Conway approached me at the launch of a Cyphers anthology late last year re editing this anthology I did not realize what was involved. I was unaware of the scale of the project and the necessity for meeting the individual writers as opposed to corresponding by emails in order to bring their work to its highest potential. My writing has been enriched by this experience.

It was a great privilege to meet the various contributors on several occasions and an honour to be allowed into their lives as they shared their work which was often sensitive and personal. I hope that I have encouraged the members of the group, many of whom are established writers, to have a reading and a writing routine, to continue to write and rewrite their work, to be aware of other art forms, be influenced by them and as McNeice commented to be aware of what the paper boys were shouting.

I congratulate the group on its publications down through the twenty nine years of its existence and in particular James Conway for his steady hand at the helm keeping the group intact.

Larkin in his poem Forget What Did states –and the empty pages / should they ever be filled / let it be with observed / celestial recurrences / the day the flowers come / and the birds go- he looked at the words, placed the right ones in the right order, like a craftsman building a dry stone wall and was never afraid to – snatch out of time the passionate transitory – as Kavanagh encouraged us to do.

From reading many of the writers in this fine anthology I can say that they are faithful to the craft.

Gerard Reidy

Contents

Notes on Contributors
List of Swan Publications

Beneath the Clock

Susan Flynn

The Moylough Belt Shrine

When a tent is folded
do whispers hang around
wafting in the dunes?

Does the pale rectangle
where sleepers pressed the machair
contain their energy?

What about shadows,
do they snag on furze bushes
when their owners leave?

Where went the power
when the man with amazing
hands passed on?

At his final sigh
did healing push out,
expand to the sky

or soak into bog
to be held by earth,
and fed to roots and feet?

When Towey's sleán, slicing
the dark turves cleanly
met with metal, what

unsayable essence
ringed within a belt
made him catch his breath?

Susan Flynn

Cosmic Time

Waves heave, swell,
pause, hold breath and
let go in climax,
a tumult of pebbles.
Curls of spume frill,
zip up the tide line.

Wet sands expand.
It is full moon tonight,
at around zenith
yipping foxes will come.
Later, some rooster will yell
at a streak of rose in the sky.

Low winter sun
eases its pale disc
onto Wicklow hills,
fingers grow numb,
the dog folds in on himself.
A chevron of Brent geese
trembles along the horizon
to rest at Bull Island.
A slow heron flaps in to roost.

The heart contracts, rests.
Breaths flow in, out,
almost in time with waves
whose sounds are all consonants
trailing into hisses.

Spring tide ebbs.
Shadow advances.
World rolls.

A train shatters the moment,
Greenwich time its servant.
Just for now though,
clock's artifice is put away,
all the senses heed
light and shadow and tide,
hunger and chilling skin.

Yesterday, parting friends
settled on the next
gathering to happen when
daffodils come into bloom.

Susan Flynn

Whisper your Secrets

We moss embossed stone pigs
are more than your glance perceives:
all the bits and pieces
of myriad lives, snowing
carbon confetti upon
the ocean floor – wishes,
worries, doubts, faiths,
sublime epiphanies –
trickled in flickering sunlight
down, down, fondled
by fronds of laminaria,
chancing off corals, noticed,
allowed pass by, to dance,
drift and lie for good
on earth's silty breast.

Embedded safe in limestone,
quarried, carried off, sculpted
in forms familiar to you
three hundred million years on
(a blink of your god's eye)
to please your visual and haptic
senses.
      Press your mouth
to our cold ears, whisper –
your secrets are safe with us.

Ruth Egan

Void

Rocks like pebbles,
the sea a pond
domesticated by the sleepy bay;
friendly clumps of seaweed
sway, obedient
to the ocean's breathing.

Deep, deep water
runs stiller
than you could ever imagine:
the chord is perfect
but the sound is cruel
to new ears
that still have dreams.

Ruth Egan

Stirring

Wet, waking, sleep-crusted world unfurl –
stretch from curl;
watch swallows tail-dipping
low over dozing cars.

Seagulls brawl, break silence
crying in a stand-off over bits of bread
their slick backs shining
under the silky drizzle.

This time is theirs
between dream and deed:
the lull before the earth
gears up and whirls away again

on a different dance.

Ruth Egan

Shape

Your shape I sense
by sight
is not the one I sense
by touch.
That one feels warm and smooth,
coveted proximity
covering me over
in featherless quilt.

Your shape by sight
I cannot grasp: now here,
now there,
the seen quickly
becoming unseen.
The eye, sleight of hand
fading into distance
of faraway lands and
plans and populace
by a peaceful sea,
while I touch
wistfully,

the two connected
only tenuously.

Brendan Devlin

Snap

It often happens so – in an instant's flicker
a some way glance – and the full sense of it hits
around the corner, on a cycling arc it struck
in twilight on a high wall against a dark blue sky
a tree that had lost its depth silhouetted
in one dimension – then the magic
a plump bird settling on its branches – fused
in an instant my eyelid closed and snapped
that image stored forever – an inadvertent gift
to render deep and make it yet replete.

Brendan Devlin

Jutted

On the gorse – sand dune
a textured eye scanned it
brailled along its surface
traced its abrasive points
there a half-ship protruding
from the sand – gorse surf
the hull only – jutted
at forty degrees – speeding
toward some mystic point

Two inverted parabolas converge
bonded at the stern-post – sealed
ochre-red-rust spreading warmth
a comforting feel of summer-time
where cloud shadows slow-glide
switch on or off its burnished red

It offers itself as sculpture – surprising
a happenchance offering more meaning
than any contrived or conscious piece
it pulses inward on its landlocked tide

Brendan Devlin

Still Life

Let this be my sacrifice – my humble gift
to art – not fruit nor flowers but stone
unearthed – not sculpted – yet sculpted now in words
a drawing forth of meanings subterranean held

Surface sand dusted – granular and abrasive
chipped in places – imperfect depths revealed
distant echoes,   deep within this stone
chiselled – no doubt from some larger block

This stone – handful sized – approximate and right
not perfect squared – nor linear straightened out
facets not crystal uniform nor pleasantly arranged
planes push – juxtapose in discordant equipoise

I would seek to set this rock – placed
just so – so that all meanings are revealed
it speaks to me – vibrates a secret sense
its history – a question posed and felt

Stephen Dineen

Compass

Dear David,

You will bury me, my son, someday far away. You'll be the responsible, eldest (maybe only) child, who'll organise the final rituals and rest me in the graveyard at St Patrick's. It's there your grandparents lie, returned to where they first met at a wedding. That's where they too married, on Christmas Eve, your grandfather going to war two days later, returning after a few years to a country that no longer recognised itself.

Long before that day we'll have time and I'll have a son to teach, inspire, perhaps befriend. And some day over an adult drink you'll look at me with those dark beady eyes you displayed today as you emerged into this thorny world, and confide in me about life's great lesson. Yes, my son, it gets very complicated.

My confession: you're not your parents' child. In your mother's mind you might be ours but on that summer night you were conceived my mind's eye saw another seeker of my children.

The dizzy world of my work takes me away a lot, surrounds me with women perfumed with the scent of danger. Amidst those sirens I've met one with whom I connect. She looks at me differently to the ephemeral lights whose breasts scream 'Yes!', who want to wrap their legs around my loins before loosening them for the final soar. It was she whom I saw as the seed finally flowed, my mind asking if anyone actually judges or cares.

Yet she never entered my mind today as the nurse revealed your raw, defenceless face. There was something of me and something of your mother in it, more your mother. And it was beauty.
Dad

*

Dear Dad,

You were born on a Tuesday, you told us once. And today, a Tuesday, we laid you to rest.

Mum told me once that a 'newness' came over you after I was born. Then, when the twins came along, apparently you wept.

At your grave this morning I returned to childhood as I remembered how we climbed the Wicklow hills, your presence evergreen by the gallant firs and pines. How secure we felt in the back of a car full of chatter, beneath the grey Sunday skies of childhood.

And there was that mischievous look you had for Mum, a grin that never left despite old age or the news she was seriously ill. 'I think we're gonna be alright,' you kept telling people after the grin subsided but neither hope nor Mum lasted long.

I remember the night before we buried her, how you approached me sheepishly after the visitors had left. 'I've a favour to ask. I know it's a little strange but will you sleep with me tonight?' you said.

'What?' I said, louder than intended.

'I haven't been alone in so long. I just need company tonight.'

I had planned to stay at home that night regardless. I couldn't refuse. And so, two grown pyjamaed men, fuzzy from wine and brandy, lay in bed, awake and acutely aware of each other's presence. Mum's stultified face washed over and over our minds.

'Was I conceived in this room?' I asked, not knowing why but knowing you were still awake.

'Yes, you were actually,' you said then paused for an aeon. 'When we found out your mum was pregnant I knew the very night.'

'Okay that's more than…'

'We were so… so alive at the time, so full of life. And then you see what it all reduces to,' and your voice dropped and drowned. I revived you and we talked about her in waves until predawn justified us abandoning the despondent hours.

The fear on your face that night told me you wouldn't last long alone. Once we'd buried Mum you were already looking east. In your early seventies, still trim and charming, you befriended Josie, a widow you'd known forty years earlier through work.

'Mum's barely in the ground and look at him!' Kim, one of the twins, said to me. I sighed, listened, described your childlike look when you'd asked me to keep vigil with you. Kim was engaged. As I relayed her uneasiness to you over a beer I realised that we had moved from father-son to friends. On the night of Kim's wedding Josie turned to you at eleven o'clock and suggested home. She could have left without you. That was harder to defend, but I too understand their powers.

Though your renewal brought surprise, your choice of resting place didn't. Amongst St Patrick's evergreens and grassy verges, near autumn's faded yellows and browns, we lowered you above Mum and your parents. The sun lying low in the sky, neither east nor west, the fresh soil fell lightly onto the box. Nothing seemed to move except one of the monkey puzzle trees, which leaned in towards the pines as though whispering to it that November is the most beautiful month of them all.

As we walked away, the day of Mum's funeral rebounded. After the post-burial reception in the village we walked home through St Patrick's. The floodlights accentuated the church's granite grandeur. An exhilarating moon illuminated the headstones and the clear and sacred night sky.

'You know we're lucky to have her here,' you said. 'Your mother had no time for graves. She wanted to be cremated. I said to her: "But wouldn't it be nice if we could sleep together forever?" She always loved the prospect of sleep! I loved when the lights went out and we candidly talked over the day. She eventually said okay.'

I think now of a shared life of conversation. Mum: consistent. You: sometimes reticent, as though hassled by lingering demons, then stridently verbose.

I've always liked the headstone that now stands above you too.
After life's battles
There are murmurings
There shall be rest

Gerry O'Donnell

God's Lough

I will drive to the high country
up to the sacred mountain
above the tainted glen of talk and thought
until the road becomes a lane, a track,
a portal into the mist wrapped scrub.

I will shed my shoes and my skin of worries
at this threshold and find my way by touch
to a hill top lit by searchlight from the veiled sun
where lies a dark lough, like a vessel of poison
held up to the lips of an absent God.

I will raise and crush a fistful of berries
let the cobalt juice of hope drip into the lough
then I will wait, as he will not come in sunlight
for he cannot look into his own eyes
kiss his own lips, drink his own face.

Only when the moon becomes a nail clipping
when all creatures are asleep and when your
breath is slower than the pull of a heavy oar
will he come and sip from his chalice
and release a single ripple.

Gerry O'Donnell

Rattlebag

They are always there, lying in wait for us
the runaways from the rattlebag of memories
hiding in fields, through train windows
like snatches of a stray dog behind a hay bale
from another time, another place, another love.

They ambush us on teeming streets
in the hollows between footfalls
in the slipstream of a sighing bus
in the after-glow of a red light pulsing slowly
In the darkroom of our mind

where we tilt and ripple developer over recesses
see a cast come back to life in the photo tray
peg a row of soft unchanging faces high on a line
watch our comedies and tragedies drip drying
smile as we dance on the ancient drops of pain.

Then, on a green light, we look down a sunlit street
and leave our darkroom wearing a most curious smile
that's caught in the blinking eye of a passing stranger
who slips it into the hip-pocket of their mind
without ever knowing why.

Gerry O'Donnell

The Perfect Match

He was a razor blade an inch from the wrist
a diamond kiss that cuts the lip
a coil of limbs on a chrome horse,

the poisoned tip of Cupid's arrow
the shadow on a fairground field
the price tag hung around passion's neck.

She was a snowstorm raging in a blue iris
a footprint dissolving under a glaze of tide
a promise whispered into a floating bottle,

the divination of a twisting curl
the swerve of an orchid in a fitful wind
the skewered heart on a crumbling wall.

He pointed a finger towards her
like the end of an unlit fuse
and she was the perfect match.

Eithne Cavanagh

Velvet Blues

A blue blue lady sings the blues.
We travel through the velvet night
just me, Billy Holiday and a bottle of booze

Gardenia lady, it's you I choose
your songs which echo my lonely plight
a blue blue lady singing the blues.

My soul is bathed in dove-like coos
caressing all stillness into flight
it's me, Billy Holiday and a bottle of booze.

Your smoky voice a melodic fuse
– connects my being to all that's quiet.
A blue blue lady sings the blues.

You sing of pain and nothing to lose,
of womanhood, race and a little moonlight,
just me, Billy Holiday and a bottle of booze.

You tell of fists and his slinky schmooze
and how he never treats you right.
A blue blue lady singin' the blues,
it's me, Billy Holiday and a bottle of booze.

Eithne Cavanagh

First Communion Rituals

Part 1

Absolved from all invented sins,
attired as Christ's mini bride
in hand-me-down dress older than me,

I picked a way through farmyard mess.
My veil was frothier than May blossom,
tiara pinked with rosebud stitchery.

Only the white sandals were new
– and the socks – lacy as cow parsley
by ditches where primroses hid.

On one side of the church
the boys looked shiny clean,
rosettes on lapels, hair spitted down.

I clutched pearly rosary beads praying
for silver-buckled-patent-leather-pumps
like all the other girls.

The following summer a sharp blade
made 'peep-toes' of my sandals
but I still yearned for Hornpipe shoes.

Part 2

Absolved from all invented sins
spray-tanned and coiffured
Christ's mini bride flounces her frills.

Her ersatz pearl tipped tiara
declares her a Princess for the day
entitled to homage from all.

Pink polished nails tap pop idol rhythms
on a simmer satin bag
plump with uncounted notes.

Above the bouncy castle she soars
as though on a white bird's wing –
new Communion shoes scythe the air.

This right of passage, digitally recorded
and saved to Cloud, proclaims the story
of a tiny celebrity at the temple of discord.

Eithne Cavanagh

Woodsmoke

The glass bangles rattle-glint
as I lift my wrist to balance
the head load of firewood.

My mother and her mother's mother
toiled this narrow hill path,
barely a breeze to whisper a sari.

My grandmother walks ahead
still lithe under her bundle of wood.
Her face is creased as a nutmeg,

the silvering plait still falls heavy
but her ankles are swollen
and flimsy sandals slither.

Over the hills woodsmoke embroiders
the sky and I pray that my daughter
and her daughter's daughter

will not know the weight balance
of firewood, the kick of loose stones;
that their wrists may gleam heavy gold.

Anne O'Neill

One Becoming the Other

Waves crash,
storm water rushes through soil to sea.

Mounds of earth
as if dropped from sky take root.

On cliff track ground squelches,
wind circles and dives.

Jackets billow, rain splashes on faces,
fingers numb.

In the distance
soft light seeps through.

Scattered rocks slowly shed their veil,
sheepishly mist retreats.

Without warning, sun shines on sea spray,
kissing the droplets, one becoming the other.

Storm's labour
silently births a rainbow.

Anne O'Neill

Letting go

Building my coffin of wood,
sawing, sanding, filing,
forward and backward motion,
the rhythmic sound of life pulsating,
hammering nails to a beat.

I had thought about what tree to use,
no specific wood or elaborate detail needed,
no preservative or finish,
one that would decompose easily,
blend seamlessly with the soil.

Wood from a tree that grows tall,
living perpendicular to the earth,
reaching out to the sky,
preparing now to lie horizontal with me,
supporting my bones in its branches.

I wonder at the possibility
of both handles and wheels,
for ease of movement,
to facilitate the body's journey, when
papers exchange for final certificate.

Perhaps I could decorate it with symbols of my life,
like 80's cloth patches sewn on rucksacks,
a hint at where the traveller has been,
Jupiter and Mars
and the planets in between.

I could carve and paint circles of words and images,
dates, memories, moments, like a frieze,
a journey through life, a letting go,
coffin as art installation,
funeral as retrospective.

Anne O'Neill

Resonance

Immersed in nature,
in this vast wilderness of time,
I catch a glimpse of what has gone
before, of life before man.
Centuries of ice tower above me
reaching back. All, is palpable.

In these pure treacherous waters,
cradling the lands of our birth,
life waters of our pre birth,
I sense you carrying me in your womb,
feel the blood of my ancestors in my veins.
Absence and presence are one.

*Calving, the glacier exhales,
ancient sounds echo, resonating
in the atmosphere, vibrating forward,
thundering and crashing into the present.
The ice bleeds, a crystal clear turquoise
marks its wounds.

All is held in this pristine whiteness.
Time stands still
in constant motion
and if I reach out,
I can almost touch you …
touch time.

*Calving: sudden release, breaking away of a mass
of ice from a glacier.

Vision Of Hell

'Clear the room –
   nothing's working. We've got no power to anything…'
   'Goddammit.'
   'Nonono.'
   'Whatever happens lads, you trained for this. Don't shoot.'
Esperansa shouted. He glanced at Ravi, immovable like a rock.
   The drumbeat rolled on like the breaking of rock and sundering
of steel.
   Hands clapped on ears and silent software activated.
   And on. Eight beats. With weight heavier than a volcano
breaking glass. Then two. Then two more. And on. Heavy. Like
that bloodied drum long-dust Khans beat when bringing death to
cities and ends to countries.
   And then it stopped.
   Blackness.

Breath was suddenly hoarse from ominous, icy air and puffs filled
the room.
   Wild glances saw exchange.
   But a light flashed in the command centre's core. Where the
captain had stood to speak ten hours distant.
   A figure rose there.
   A little girl.
   Shine shadowed her.
   'What…' said one techie.
   Hands were still being clicked. Questions asked. And being
answered by a mute, heavy silence. Heavy like a world.
   Her stare shivered all watchers.
   Her perfect white skin betrayed not a blemish.
   Until it did. A little crimson dot on her forehead. And it grew.

To a puddle. Blood. Oozing from her ears. Her eyes. Her mouth. And other places. Cries erupted from her. Hands returned to ears.

And her face contorted. Her body shifted painfully. Like a great maggot being born inside her breaking to be free. Her screams filled the room. And it did. And none save one could help but look away. She flew apart.

A crimson shower masked the floor.

Limbs emerged. Long like a mantis. Moving. Writhing. Thin, impossibly thin. Almost a man but not. Its face recognisably a face but not. Its skin ivory white with eyes only for places sunless and rank. With fingers and toes like boned worms.

It screamed. Howling with pitch batlike and sirens call. And it went on like a one-note orchestra, Captain's skin shaking at the sound, glasses nearby trembling and teeth gritting under the pressure. His stomach heaved. Its face bent and played like a joker mask folding.

Then maggots. Insects. Legs eight and six with hair darker than star vacuum and eyes that blazed black. Snapping. Grinding. Eating. Like the sound of maggots on flesh and the crunch of teeth on bone.

And the heap fell.

What more? What to do? Captain breathed heavy. What to do. Something burst from the floor. The first he saw was wings. Ribbed chest ten times the size of a man.

And the wings. Batlike yet not, like some ancient dead thing drawn from worlds long cursed of life. From evolution lines far from any known. But familiar.

Coals for eyes. Blade-sharp claws piercing deck like mud. Red dark skin roiling in bodies whipped in agonies endless and endless. The wall bent around it. Like it was folding. Its teeth measured feet. White yet bloody. Deepest dark and blackest nightmare.

It howled. But different from before. Primal still yet deeper. Things moved down that throat. None wanted to know.

Thin and wicked and cruel. It dripped crimson. The breath was not real. Dead was the closest description, but even that would have told only a tenth of the tale. Bloodstink and tears were its background.

Only three vomited at that. Only one burst to tears. Till then.

But its chest was growing. Writhing. Something bursting to be free. There was a buildup of pressure like a kettle almost overblowing or a balloon about to burst.

What more?

The creature screamed yet more.

A – paw … fist? punched from it. And something emerged.

A figure. Ire and crimson spattered.

Blood and ire and things came off it like shed skin.

Its footsteps drummed forward.

The deck splashed akin to dark water where the ground blackened beneath its feet.

Its eyes shifted. From crimson, wroth things with fire for rings to hollow cavelets, with sockets gone and only the briefest insane glance of the inside. To darkest night. To sheet white glinting like stars. Back to sockets. Then red. Only red.

And its skin. Or surface. A black-white and all between shifting colour far off description and spectrum. And there were movements on that surface. Mouths. Opening and closing like the respiring of a beast. And roiling, sharp glinting things. Teeth and claw and poisonous paining objects drawn from ten thousand worlds, the effort of evolution's cruelty toil beyond count. Bodies roiled torturously in unknown suffering across that torso. Like hell. In flesh.

And it was… what? Male? Almost recognisably Male. Seven foot yet somehow taller. And so more.

Its mouth opened. And teeth yet violent and fierce sawed there.

The walls shivered at it.

And then dark fire erupted from the figure. Like a candle. Lashed the ceiling and spread along like the view of water from the black down below.

Black light shone like a searchlight from that figure. The sound was cries and motion. Wheel and cog. Fully savage and deeply primal. Yet steady and solid. Like an engine that knows not surcease. Seemingly distant shadowed things on the walls seemed to reach for it. Screams were its singsong.

It was ferocity.

Most of the staff were long seeking cover. Muniz shook.

All gods and devotions saw rounding in people's prayers, like paper pieces before a storm.

'Mele save us…'

Ten thousand hours, hell, a lifetime's worth of discipline. All gone beneath this. This thing which reached with effort past countless lessons from schoolyard to school of life, to the stuff of nightmare and reddest thought at the pit of soul. Those terrors and things all kept locked through wisdom. Through learning. Through growing. It ungrew them.

And it was easily, effortlessly too much.

And Ravi screamed. His hand tensed round his weapon. And fired. He never had time to regret it.

Christine Hughes

Fête Day

Fanfare for the fête
let the fudge-making begin.
Sweet drudgery, no grudging the outlay.
Store up butter, sugar, condensed milk.
Then turn silk to indulgent velvet.
Gently melting, easy and slow
then plip-plopping and popping,
raging and fuming, gurgling and burbling.
Discrete parts yield to the heat.
Crunchy demerara is shushed, brittle crystals melt.
Brown, white and yellow unifying and tanning,
dark streaks beaten back into the blend.
Languid caramel-fragrant steam undulates
above the churning brew.
Yearning now to finish, check and re-check
the temperature and the texture.
Sluggish, it thickens, folding and pleating,
clinging to the pan; weary but undefeated.
Decision made, turn off the flame.
Continue to stir and push
until it's time to heave the resistant blanket
on to the paper-lined bed.
It stretches and drowses,
luxuriating and seductive.
Busy tongues lick cooling spoons.
Score and cut, bag and tie.
Await the day, anticipate delight.

Mary Guckian

Visiting St. Columba's Hospital

On Legion of Mary visits to ladies
who looked old with hairy chins
and grey worn out hospital gowns –
quiet, silent they looked fragile.
We stayed for two hours with
our grubby religious magazines
attempting conversation, yet these
women wanted to finger the cotton
material in our flowery dresses.
Our own clothes valuable and
would never think of parting with
the few garments we had made.

When I remember them, it makes
me sad that I never read them
a story or maybe a funny poem.
Left to linger in a locked away
place, like so many thousands
of other women who were sent
to Mother and Baby Homes,
Magdalene Laundries and other places
to hide their pregnancies, have
their babies snapped from them
and pay for their sorrows by
scrubbing floors and washing
clothes by hand without any
payment or celebration.

The greatest sadness – they
could never trace the places
where their babies were sent
not even in later life, dying
without ever an embrace
for their lovely lost children.

Mary Guckian

Milking Cows in Summer

We walked towards the lake field
with scoured buckets in our hands.
Enjoying soft green mossy grass
where winter flooding left growth.
Our tiny toes comforted after walking
across higher ground where thistles
stung us and pushed sharp needles
into the fragile soles of our feet.

Sometimes, Francie sang songs
and the melodious tunes travelled
across the water as he cut hay
with the mowing machine sounding
like background music or he might
be saving his oat crop, a swishing
sound keeping up with his words.

Reaching our cows they were quiet,
waiting for us to take the weight
from the over flowing udders.
Chewing the cud while we pulled
the tits and filled our buckets.
Heading back over bumpy fields
we go home, straining healthy
liquid into disinfected muslin.

Margaret Zheng

Winter Moon

Leaves lie forlorn
on heavy trod pavements
sulphurous, menopausal.
My stale breath
hangs limply in
the cold air,
bitter, stultifying.

Frost chokes
the green tender grasses
while loneliness stalks me
but in the swirling mists
I catch the glint
of the moon
distant in the night sky.

Solitary open eyed,
ringed with a certain
effervescence.
Instantly I find my mouth
has curved with the effort
to devour its splendour
and claim it as my own.

Margaret Zheng

Stone

Mossy stones lie smocked in summer glory
along sedges of upturned walls, creamery lids and things
strapped into our churlishness
as we gadded about engulfed in teenage angst.

On trips back they lie there abandoned
or seamed into old forgotten spaces.
It was all I could do not to touch their hollowed backs
and let their earnestness seep into my soul

Margaret Zheng

Sheep

Whorls of flesh
bluster about the moors
looping their way
softly soft
around scutted grasses.
Coils of togetherness
locked into the upholstery
of mossy rocks
and bruckeldy heather.

Guzzlers of whins
lie in a stupor
from the mid-day sun.
There is ne'er a sound
save for the odd clunk
of a John Deere
thridding its way
through the thin-necked pass,
its green hood
bursting through
the symmetry
of hump-backed marshes
nestling great big lobes
of jocular flesh.

Valerie Collins

Motorway Meltdown

Sadie was not a motorway driver even though she had spent decades driving around Dublin city in all sorts of cars: people carriers when her children were at school, then graduating to regular size cars as they left. Her current companion was a 2003 centenary model black Ford Fusion she called Doris. They made a good team and had sussed out all the short-cuts on their regular routes thus avoiding the main roads and heavy traffic. Still they never went over 50 kph with traffic lights punctuating any decent stretch of road that might tempt them to let rip.

However this cosy routine was about to come to an end as Sadie's job was changing location from the city centre to a more salubrious green site on the outskirts, necessitating a drive on the motorway to get there. As if by way of protest Doris had of late begun to stall and splutter so Sadie was relieved that the annual maintenance check-up was due, but she knew that the real obstacle was her fear of speed that had plagued her driving life.

She discussed the matter with her husband Joe who was himself retired, and lived a simple life planting a meadow in his back garden and doing the Irish Times crossword on-line every day. He drove a neat Hyundai i20 and Sadie loved to sit next to him as he sped along the motorway overtaking with confidence and maintaining a speed of 100 kph with ease on their various outings.

"I'll just have to quit the job! Anyway I only had another two years to go to retirement." Sadie said by way of conclusion.

"Well that's a bit extreme," Joe countered, trying to get his wife to see reason.

"You have the whole summer to go before school is back and I can give you some more lessons on the M50. If that doesn't work you can go to a driving school. You can take the Hyundai and if worse comes to worse I can always drive you in."

"Thanks for the encouragement and your faith in me Joe but

you know Doris and me are inseparable," Sadie said heading into the kitchen to start the dinner. As she put some chops under the grill the memory of 'the spasm' episode resurrected itself. The potatoes got a good scrubbing as she relived that night-time drive home on the motorway with Joe beside her and their teenage son Hugh in the back. Her accelerator leg developed a spasm which became so severe that she had to slow down and exit the motorway; then driving around the lonely streets of an unfamiliar suburb in the silent car and Joe's remark that broke the silence:

"How's the spasm?"

"You know sarcasm doesn't help in a tough situation," she called in to Joe who was doing his accounts at the other end of their new open-plan living space. But as she was always telling him once the extractor fan is turned on you can't hear a thing. So she turned her attention instead to chopping the carrots.

Summer to Sadie meant time spent sitting in the back garden reading novels, meeting up with friends, going on a holiday and getting some shape on the house. One of her pleasures was seeing duvets drying in the sun; the chore of cleaning all the windows in the house brought satisfaction, but heading up to the M50 for practice runs, even though it was top of the to-do list kept dropping. They did eventually make a few attempts and while the journeys were accomplished the cost to her nervous system was high, and it was a relief to head off to the West on holidays.

Then as the nights grew longer the summer days vanished and Sadie was due back in work. She loved her job as a Special Needs Assistant in a secondary school and she got great enjoyment helping the students in her care so quitting was never a realistic option. On the first morning she kissed Joe goodbye although he was still asleep, said a prayer to her guardian angel, and headed for the motorway in a rejuvenated Doris sparkling for the previous day's valeting.

The drive up to the entry point was nerve-racking negotiating the large roundabout then getting in line for the final lap before the descent. The drivers revving their engines reminded Sadie of bucking broncos getting ready to burst through their stalls into the rodeo arena. Her heart was leaping in her chest, her hands were sweating as she gripped the steering wheel, but luckily her leg wasn't cramping as that would have been a disaster.

Then they were off. No turning back. No room for error. It was time to merge. Sadie's prayers turned audible as they went into the fray. Cars were zooming all around them, but she held Doris steady at 80 kph on the inside lane. They were overtaken repeatedly and Sadie figured most cars were doing at least 100 kph as they zoomed up behind them before changing lanes at the last minute. The thought came into Sadie's head of whether she could sustain the momentum but she let it go as quickly and stayed focused on the road. Glancing into the rear view mirror she saw a gigantic truck descending upon them at maximum speed and knew instinctively that it was make or break time.

"Come-on Doris we can do it, we're a team," Sadie said to her feisty friend, increasing their speed enough to avoid the juggernaut wiping them off the road. It stayed right behind them as though it knew that this was a significant outing and they needed a powerful nudge. The speedometer reached 100 kph, which must have satisfied the truck as it suddenly pulled back. Sadie realized she had let go of the panic and was enjoying the challenge. "We're cruising Doris," she shouted, the smile on her face spreading all the way to her right leg. "There's no stopping us now."

The sun shone down on the oncoming hills, and the road before them was there for the taking.

Michael Thurlow

Moving On

We seldom think about dying. Richard – never Dick – Rooney, certainly isn't doing so. He is trying to impress the woman he's with, I'd say. Lots of gesturing, laughing, a real good time I'd say. But he is going to die. Tonight. I haven't quite decided how but it'll come to me. Probably in his car, but not if she goes with him. No innocents involved. Joanne wouldn't want that. So if Richard gets lucky he gets doubly lucky.

I am sitting a mere three tables away from him but he can't see me. Neither can anyone else of course. Too wrapped up in his chat-up to notice anybody but her anyway, although there is another couple with them. Do they have any idea that he's a killer? I doubt it. Not that it matters. He knows. He mightn't remember too clearly the night he came speeding along High Street, but he and his family spent enough money hushing it up over the next few weeks. His 'beamer' was barely scratched. Oh he knows alright.

The woman even looks a bit like Joanne. Classy she was, my Joanne. Soft black hair curling down to bare shoulders, brown eyes that could draw you in until eventually the volcano erupted, if you were allowed to get that close. We were married for two short, short years. She was pregnant with Seán, or Shona, depending. We didn't want to know, so Seán for a boy or Shona for a girl. The autopsy showed it was a Seán.

Dick is guzzling beer I can see. He was on the wagon for a token period after the court case. He'd been banned from driving twice and still he got probation. Jesus! How can that be? A good family, remorse, rehab, community service, all that shit. He's in some expensive hotel, which pretends it's a hospital for drunks, while Joanne and Seán are in Palmerstown Cemetery. I'll kill him slowly.

If he drives home alone I'll sit behind him and when I think it's time I'll tip him on the shoulder. One look at the wreck of my face should do it. It terrifies me, and I'm dead.

They're wrapping up now. Bugger, she's getting into his car. She has no idea how big a risk she's taking. Maybe she deserves… no, Joanne wouldn't allow that, and to be honest I'd agree. Dick is laughing, relaxed, fearless. He really should be called Dick.

I stand in the shadows while they make the bed move. It does nothing for me. I'm just biding my time. When they fall asleep I move over and stand beside him. He moves, perhaps sensing me. He moans, nightmares. Good. Maybe I won't kill him for a while. Nocturnal visits and night terrors. Not enough though. He must die, in his death is justice.

He screams and sits up. I jump back, startled, even though he can't see me. The woman shouts, "what the fuck?" A bit coarse for my liking.

"I killed them, I killed them…", he whimpers. He is shaking violently.

"What are you talking about?" she asks, "it's only another bad dream, Richard." Now she is sympathetic. Never been big on male vulnerability as a chick-magnet myself, but it calms him. It seems he's had nightmares before, and also that this not her first time to comfort him.

Dick turns to her. It seems he has made a decision.

"I haven't been totally honest with you about the accident."

Accident my arse Dickie. You murdered us. But he doesn't hear me, of course, and continues to whinge.

"I was out of my mind on coke and every sort of drink you can think of. I should never have been anywhere near a car that night."

He starts crying again, and to my own amazement I find myself thinking he seems genuine. I don't care. He's still dying, if not tonight, soon.

"But Richard, you went to rehab, you stopped drinking and doing drugs, you're not that person anymore."

"I'm alive, and they're dead because of me. She was pregnant for God's sake! I didn't even get a scratch. How can that be, how can it be?" His body shakes with the strength of his sobs.

50

"Richard, you've spent your time since then helping every charity, you've worked with drunks, and you haven't had a drink. You have to move on."

Hasn't had a drink? What was I watching tonight? Was I wrong? It occurs to me that he drove without any sign of drunkenness, spoke without slurring. Maybe I was wrong.

"None of it counts for shit, Shona." He shudders again and she throws an arm around him. What a picture. The irony of her name is truly gut-wrenching. If I still had guts.

I feel my bitterness ebbing away. I want to cling to it but I can't. Instead of a slow painful death, he is condemned to a guilt-racked life. Something changes in me and I look towards the window where hints of dawn can be seen in the change from black to gray. I drift towards the morning, leaving Dick to whatever life throws at him. I don't wish him well.

I should be surprised, but somehow I'm not – outside there is a beautiful woman waiting.

Joanne has found me at last, or I have found her. Whichever it is, we glide away together.

Rose McBride

The Crime

What now for the birds
the tall trees are gone,
where will the pigeons
do their wooing
their throaty cooing
where will the collared doves land
the black-white-teal magpies stand
where will the crows
and cousin jackdaws gather
the singing thrush
the blackbird sway
now the trees are gone away?

For days the birds circled
making not a sound
looking for their trees
lying dead on the ground
cut down in their prime
because the residents
said it was time.
they argued it was not a crime –
by law they were entitled to light.

Now, it's like restored sight
but what about the birds?
no more nesting
no more song.

The trees are gone.

Marion Kerrigan

Childhood Journey

We left for the seaside in the maroon Anglia
it was an annual day in August
speeding along colourful roadside
arriving at the sea in a gust.

Run, run to the beach
August my favourite month
cherishing childhood memories
run, run barefoot.

Sun shone gloriously in full burst
water ripples call us to sea
the whistling kettle on the gas stove
as we played on the sand "bi-jove".

Oh! How I longed for this day
playfully crashing the bumper cars
daunting experiences on the chairoplanes
looking down from heaven's stars.

Back on earth splash in the sea
time to break the chord with this joy
now to re-trace our journey
home to dwell on next year's party.

John Hyland

Ten Fourteen

Revolving wheels in mid-July
propelled one towards Howth Hill on high
Enroute Boru's Clontarf was seen
evoking thoughts of 1014.

Far off green hills drew Viking eyes
to see themselves neath Irish skies
pillage Celtic treasures rare
from cloistered cells of peace and prayer.

Land leapers with their long boats moored
were into Clontarf's battle lured
denouement came for Norse and Dane
as Dalcassian Tribes without the strain

on Good Friday long the battle raged
as mortal blows each side did trade
high tide swelled the Gaelic breast,
much raiders blood lost in conquest.

Victorious Emperor of the Gaels
King Brian retired to tended vales
but fatal strokes from fleeting Dane
saw Boroimhe, eviscerated, slain,
twelve nights passed waking Irish dead
heroic Brian rests in Armagh bed.

Elaine Beverley Tyrrell

A Footnote in History

Two years after the Cuban Missile Crisis of 1962, I was a child of about 6 years on board the Irish Shipping cargo ship "The Irish Rowan". My father, Captain Ivan Tyrrell was her Master Mariner at the time. We made History by being the first Irish ship to enter a Russian port as well as the first Irish ship to bring grain from America to Russia despite the raging of the Cold War.

Despite the warring publicly between both aggressors, behind the scenes a pragmatic deal had been done between the Americans and the Russians. It was called "The American-Russian Agreement". It had been initiated by President John F. Kennedy in 1963 prior to his assassination. The reason this deal was done was as follows. On the one hand, there had been such a bumper wheat harvest in America that year that supply exceeded demand and accordingly the American grain farmers were having particular difficulty in selling their produce. On the other hand, the Russian harvest during the same year had been spectacularly bad leading to a food shortage and Russian people starving. So despite the fact that the Americans and the Russians were publicly at loggerheads at the time, the two opposing sides arrived at a trade agreement whereby grain was exported to Russia from America. Because Ireland was officially a neutral country, the former semi-state body Irish Shipping won a contract to transport the grain from America to Russia. My father happened to be Master of the "Irish Rowan" when we brought grain from an American port to Nakhodka in Russia. I can still recall a bit of those times which proved to be "A Footnote In History!"

Ref.http://homepage.eircom.net/~Irishshipping/The%201960's. htm

Denise Ryan

The Falling Finch

A shivering finch, searches for food
in the rising snow, its stubby beak thinly tapping
the Koch curve of snowflake, a gladius of piercing frost
protrudes from his narrow tail. The wind hardens
and the grey sky scrolls back to blackness.

Gulls with their throats half cut
hover in awestruck intensity, looking
for the sharpened edge of bread, the tiny finch
is outnumbered his body spelling death in the snow.

Earth worms sleep deep, in soiled cots,
untouched by the weightless sleeve of hail.
There is nothing between the earth
and the frozen snow, only damp sprouting eyes of silence
gawping helplessly at his bundled hunger.

Along the edge of my garden, a trench of haunting tracks
find shelter from their sunken self.
Grabbing a fist of golden cereal, I sprinkle them in my footprints.
The shivering finch ascends, in a chariot of flaxen light,
to feed and restore in my impression.

Denise Ryan

Knowing

Let me snug into the warm space
your back has lovingly shaped,
memories of his tired muscles speak
through a hundred thread counts.
Unpaid bills close their gaping mouths
and chores disguise themselves as art.
Our composition is tightly drawn
between the folds of our skin, feeling
the stares embalm our shattered feet.

I wrap my arms around his waist,
feeling his spine wedge between my knees.
The columns of his shoulders cave in,
surrendering his arms to sleep.
His legs loosen like light on ripples
his face dissolving into darkness.
A soft arch of breathing rises above
the night's silence, becoming a union
of breath in a lagoon of submission.

Coiling like a spool of wool, I sink
into the hemispheres of his curved form,
hatching a million kisses on his tender lobe
my secrets drowning in the canal of his ear.
His hair smells of sweet roasted almonds,
but my heart hungers for the truffles in his eyes.
His heavy head flops like a bear's paw
on the soft pillow. His weary bones
crying out like wooden dolls.

Denise Ryan

Moon

Do you shine wholesome & bright over Syria?
diffusing your glossy lens over weeping jasmine.
Their infant whimpers echo from the rubble,
bleeding an effigy of dust.
Mothers claw the earth to tender their petals,
beneath cloaks of brittle shrapnel.
Kites of smoke drift like doomed angels
as the world looks on at its unborn self.

Are you an endless waxing gibbous?
Coiled in shame on its grieving cliffs,
sacrificing your fullness for the blinded west.
Your bulbous eyes blazing, through the benzene
black sky, your lambent rising & falling
in an endless depth of death.

Brid Fitzpatrick

Ancestral Rath

Trees dance
in the circle
of the ring fort.
Their leafy boughs
conjuring up the
past to present times.
Buried the memories
of the hearth and soil;
of cattle warming the
sleeping dwellers on a
winter's night.
The wolf and owl
calling from amid the
ancestral trees.
I wondered did
the people see through
the wattle walls or
splutter to open
the door when smoke
rose to the roof.
Perhaps if pottery lies
beneath, we can touch
their craft and work
and then dance on the
flagstones of their hearth.

Shirley Gorby

Inside

Outside my window
I hear sounds
of children fighting
screaming at each other
let him go, let him go
but when I look
no children, only birds
maybe fifty in the field
gathered in circles.

But I heard words,
children's words.
What if the children
are inside the birds
and the birds don't realise
that something human
is within them –
something not of their world
is nestling inside of theirs.

Rachael Stanley

Atoms

Stretching into infinity,
the atoms and molecules of potential
hide in empty space,
become textures, colours, flesh, language.
Then form into sentences upon tongues
that will one day return to a realm
beyond names and descriptions,
beyond labels and conditioned minds,
and dance their way back to infinity.

Rachael Stanley

Cat and Mouse

When death comes knocking on my door
she will ask me if I'm ready and perhaps
I'll tell her to go away or I may
say, yes I am ready for oblivion.

She might chuckle to herself,
ha ha, she is going to be in for such a surprise
when she discovers I'm only a phantom, just
an ending of a one act play.

She might be careful not to let me
overhear her, she could say,
no point making her over familiar with me
while she is still alive with this thing called
life coursing through her veins.

Perhaps I should pull the plug on her,
take her by surprise, not give her any
time to think, or to welcome me,
nor time to die before she dies,
to become a pure vessel for emptiness.

Rachael Stanley

Fear

From where does it spring?
Often I am assailed by dark pockets
as I greet a new day.
It clutches me in the gut.

From where does this enemy come?
The unconscious terrors that have no
recognizable form, that lie
in ambush waiting for me.

What store of memories do I carry?
At times futility overwhelms me.
All this abundant life that forms
into concrete matter and then dissolves.

Does the solution lie in embracing
the nothingness, in emptying oneself
and stripping away – entering the
vast realm formless and pure?

Michael Gavin

Arboreal Salvation

The falling leaves speak of death
the long nights tell of short days
the frosted air of lack of hope
but soon the spring will come
singing the joy of rebirth
long days and warming nights
what more can a soul seek?

Yet I continue
my myriad journeys
finding not solace in light or lack
the flower follows its programme
without care or question
and so I ask God
If you truly loved me
why was I not made a tree?

Margaret Thomas

Landing Window

Sharp lines shorten my horizon
white lights glow in angular shapes
through frames dotted along that block
the cloyingness of lives between the Canals
framed by darkness I wonder briefly
at the beings beyond this silent alignment.

Tayo Odelade

Naturalisation Ceremony

And slowly but surely, reality sinks in. I did not expect the ceremony itself to matter too much to me. It was just a technicality after all. It was simply formalising a feeling, a relationship long there. The overwhelming emotion, the sadness, the emptiness, did not quite catch me unaware, but highlighted a fact that had been beaten to the back of the mind.

You, who would have felt the weight and significance of the day, were not there. Not through any fault of your own, but I missed you. Your happiness and relief for me. What you would have said about its significance in my life. Our chat on what you would wear to the ceremony, and what you would not say about what I wore to it. I did not want friends there, as it should have been you. I was too scared to ask your oldest daughter to be there, imagining her rebuke to such a request. I could not ask your youngest son to take time off, from something he desperately needed currently. I just wanted someone that felt a little like you, where I thought you should be. I took pictures for you. They're simple and unimaginative, but I thought of taking them home and showing them to you. You would have been so happy to see them. Still thinking of you. I love you, and hope you realise that. Please rest, and don't worry about us, about me. I'll get there step by step.

Margaret Boles

Homs – Houla

The Assyrian came down...
what did you do in the war, Gran?
what did you do in the war, Mum?
what did you do in the war, Dad?
The Assyrian came down...
but this is not George Gordon's war,
this is not Lord Byron's war,
technically, this is not yet even
a war, and yet they come down
like a wolf on the fold
to the children of Homs,
the children of Houla.
Did the cohorts gleam
in the purple and gold
of Syrian government
approval for the massacre
of young children?
Meanwhile, war weary
international communities
shuffle about ineffectually.
It seems there's no sanctions,
no actions to be taken
to prevent the destruction.
Ashur's women will continue
their weeping for children,
while Afghanistan seems like Vietnam;
all I can do is pen this poem,
hoping those with power,
will prove themselves effective
in preventing another Houla, another Homs.

Fred Lalor

Rest one Bird

Have you ever seen
a bird on a bicycle,
coasting on its wings.

Not having to cycle
but it moves along
all it does is sings.

It sits in the back
behind a saddle,
in a cage tied on by string.

Some say it's lazy
some say it's crazy,
it's one of those things.

Dominic O'Neill

Too Long Didn't Read

Sometimes people are a captive audience. Bored – but too polite to say it. You can't tell when you have droned on too long.

An old priest said a sermon should be like a miniskirt. Long enough to cover the essentials – and short enough to maintain interest.

And one day the rules change. There is no longer social pressure to go to mass. Or (to take another example) history is dropped from the Inter Cert.

Our friend Ted, the history teacher, is incensed: 'It is very hard to learn history with all the pressure on time. They chop off history to put in something useful like computer science.' He added, 'Our attention spans are getting shorter and shorter. It is to do with smart phones and computers. In the smart phone world everything is dismissed or shortened down. Everything is telescoped into a smaller and smaller space all the time.'

It is so easy to bore people. Ted the historian says you can tell when the class of young ladies is uninterested. 'They let you know. They flop over the desk, like a puppet with its strings cut. But in school the teacher has to work to the speed of the slowest. And the faster kids are rolling their eyeballs. They use the Americanism, MEGO (My Eyes Glazed Over), and the dismissive 'Whatever' – a verbal shrug of the shoulders.'

Father Aiden joined Ted and me outside the church. 'Priests are now downloading their sermons from Google instead of writing their own,' says Father Aiden.

The next mass had started. With a different priest, droning on and on. 'He's very fond of the sound of his own voice, he is,' said Ted the historian. Father Aiden was too loyal to agree with us.

Father Aiden gets very annoyed when I speak in praise of short sermons. He scowls like a four year old. If you can't say something in three or four minutes, you probably can't say it at all. Mark

Twain said about sermons, 'Few are saved after the first twenty minutes'.

Father Aiden retaliated by chiding me for reading too many poems at a Christmas Party. 'They say 'Go on, go on, read us another poem' but that is only politeness.'

Ouch. I was stung, 'Politeness or hypocrisy'.

Ted the historian sympathised 'Some see politeness as hypocrisy. I prefer to see it as kindliness: they haven't the heart to hurt you.' Ted ran for senator once. 'Didn't I get promised a grand pile of votes. I was sure I'd get in. Not a bit of it. Didn't the electors, when cornered, agree with each candidate in turn. When it came to the polling booth it was another story'

We don't like bluntness as a nation. 'That dress doesn't suit you'. Not the kind of thing people like to hear. Mankind can stand but little truth. (I shivered after the restaurant in Terenure closed after a bad review in 'The Irish Times').

Father Aiden said 'After a dreadful meal we will say 'Grand, grand': 'How was it?' 'Lovely lovely. Grand grand.'

Young people are more blunt and dismissive.

'I sent you an e-mail.'

'TLDR'. Too Long, Didn't Read.

I'd start to tell my younger daughter something: 'Did I ever tell you ....' 'Yes.'

I tell my older daughter about Mugabe, or the Berlin Wall, or the fall of Yugoslavia, and she gently says, 'Dad, is this stream of consciousness?'

She is no longer doing history.

History is a thing of the past.

Paul Turner

Lesson

We headed out of Vegas that morning, seeking the 95 Freeway, our destination, Mammoth Lake. They say every day is a school day, and today's lesson came early. In California a black nozzle on a garage pump, denotes petrol, a green one diesel, the opposite of home. I gave a squeeze of the pump trigger, from filling the Harley with diesel, an expensive learning exercise.

After our refuelling near miss, we quickly found the 95, and the last of Vegas gave way in a flash, the road becoming a straight arrow pointing through the bleak desert. We felt good........for a while! It soon became obvious however, that doing cocktails till 4 A.M. wasn't the best preparation for this motorcycle ride. The heat rose quickly, and we soon felt its effects. We pulled over for a water break, and decided to stop at the next town, Indian Springs. I had studied our route on the internet the night before, and it looked like a big town. It turns out what I saw on the map was mostly a military base, very off limits to joe public. The actual town, was away off the road, so we decided to wait till the next place, Amargossa Valley.

The traffic we met was sporadic, mostly trucks, as we rumbled on, in the increasing heat. Another twenty miles passed, and Penny started to feel worse. To get to our destination, we could either skirt around Death Valley, or go via Tonopah, two hundred miles away. We stopped for more water, water that never tasted so good. We scanned the horizon for any sign of the next town. Eventually a manmade structure appeared in the flat desert bleakness. It was a billboard, and simply declared, in big red capital letters "BROTHEL". Yes, the human habitation in Amargossa Valley, consists of a gas station, a legal brothel, and a supermarket that sells souvenir t-shirts that celebrate the nearby secretive, 'Area 51', plastered with aliens, with logos like, "shh, don't tell anyone I live out here." We pulled up at the supermarket and stumbled inside. Penny was suffering. We grabbed more water and started to think about our next move. We discussed turning back to Vegas in the evening, and riding back to Newport Beach early the next day. I asked someone if a bus goes to Tonopah. The man stared blankly at me, as though the word bus, was some unfamiliar foreign word. Penny was in tears now, as we sat outside and debated our options. We came up with a plan. All we needed, was a good Samaritan, with four wheels, going in the right direction. People were either going one way, or the other, it couldn't be hard to blag a lift. We just needed someone who was willing to help, preferably not a serial killer. Soon we had our first offer of assistance. He was going the wrong way however. A few minutes later we attracted another offer. Jackpot!, not only did he seem like a decent harmless older man, but he was going all the way to Tonopah.

Five minutes later, I was riding on ahead, while Penny sat back in air-conditioned luxury, the desert, to her, now a harmless scene through tinted windows. Penny chatted away to our new friend, and was so engrossed in conversation, she didn't notice the unusual nature of the next town. Goldfield was established during the goldrush, and was once home to 30,000 people. It now has about 200, but hasn't changed much in appearance, complete with old style houses and saloons. Some very old cars complete the picture, in an amazing dusty desert time capsule.

Our friend, it turned out, was going further than Tonopah. We had to part company though at 'Coaldale'. We met a fork in the road after Tonopah, and I enquired in a gas station about the right road to 'Coaldale'. The Asian shop assistant, didn't have very good English, and replied "cold day, how is it a cold day?". No, I repeated, "Coaldale, it's a place". He got angry and said, "cold day, it's cold at night, but how is this cold?" I gave up.

Another man fixing a car, confirmed that we were on the right road. Coaldale, it turned out, is just a junction in the middle of nowhere. We posed for a photo with our rescuer, and swapped contact details. He departed and the two of us stood at the junction chatting, when a car appeared from nowhere, behind us. It was a police car, with a sole officer inside, complete with yogi bear type ranger hat. "you folks alright there" he drawled. We both started to babble like a pair of 5 year olds, explaining very badly about our day. The cop enquired why the bike was parked on the road. The verge consisted of a pile of loose gravel, difficult to negotiate on a 900 lb motorcycle. He didn't get it, but didn't get too upset. Eventually he just said "so everybody is o.k. then?". The car disappeared in a cloud of dust, and we were alone again.

Onward to Mammoth Lake, which came quicker than we expected. The landscape changed suddenly, and the climate too, as we climbed into the hills. Flat stony desert became cool green forest, and soon we reached our hotel, a fake Austrian Tyrolean style lodge. We checked in, looking tired and scruffy. Penny did the deal at reception, and when we enquired about places to eat, the man at the desk put us right, adding just one little piece of information, that left a disbelieving expression on her face, that I will never forget.

He mentioned that there were bears roaming the town and casually told her if we met one while out walking, to just point at it and say in a firm, but commanding voice "bear go home"!

Every day is indeed a school day, and this one had been long, and full of interesting lessons!

Philomena Conway

Waterman

By the seashore
at Curracloe
paddling in
the golden sand
while my waterman
swims to the rhythm's
bounce, dance and
music of the waves.

May we have many
more years together
listening
to the music
of the sea and
feel the magic
of the golden sand.

James Conway

Queen of the birds
(For Philomena)

The words mean
a passport to where
love conquered death.

A message from my frail
soul, always in awe
of her truth, her strivings.

Remember love woven
in the heart is worth more
than a thousand dreams –

Consecrated, I hold onto
memory, as rain splashes
on recall: castaway I am

stronger now, my old bones
hold me up, as the year
ends dark days will come

to test what's left of my breath.
In feathered gentility, I recall her
'Queen of the birds'
the words come like
invisible ink on a sky
the colour of murmurings.

One whisper with the lips
I have left.

James Conway

Snatched Away

'The Aran Islands', she said:
the excitement still in her
eyes – her memory made me
dream of a black curragh

in a wheat field under an Artist's
sky where the blue light of her day
met the blue light of mine.
Now that I have lost her;

pain and entanglement scatter
the pepper seeds of yesterday.
With the lithe of lightning
I grasp the nucleus of her memory.

In the black curragh sheened
with rain we row to safety
where a cottage with white walls
and a warm fire with turf wafting

into the thin evening pulls us in
where she nestles beside me,
her own beautiful scent is all
I desire, as last hours are snatched away.

James Conway

A Seventh Sense

She can break the ice
no ice pick needed
she can get to each root
see each beginning coming,
festering in the ground
in the head or in the hand.

A seventh sense dances in
her, a knowing radar lifts
her eyes above the tallest man.
Give her a problem to chew
upon, a something those who
are paid a sea of dollars to sort
out; the world's problems, hunger,
deprivation, the curse of inbred
hatred, any of a thousand puzzles
she can, she will sort out their knots
like cousined computers who whine
and speak in their robotic languages

of "You are veering near the edge, come
back, let this little lady do your sums!"

Christine Broe

High-visibility

At Harold's Cross this morning
I saw a boy coated in light,
in a yellow jacket so luminous
he made November bright.

Like beacons I saw more coming,
walking with mothers and prams,
some in seats on the back of bikes
some cycled, some skated, some ran.

They shone through the gloom
of side roads and of the leafless park,
and coming across canal bridges
they even made swans look dark.

A place that once housed orphans
is now besieged with joy,
children emerge from the darkness,
clothed in light, every girl, every boy.

Arriving from all directions
at St Clare's gate they cluster around.
I wish I could be an eye in the sky,
see that yellow star shine on the ground.

Christine Broe

One Curved Feather

My pockets filled with bread
my head with Eucharistic delusions,
I set out to feed flocks of birds.

I had a vision of how it would be
as the bread flew from my hands
in an arc over the water,
how those birds would descend
a great white swirl of wingspans, tail fans,
from the bridge, from the roofs,
how my spirit would rise with them, fly.

But they had moved to the next bridge
where students at the lock gates
donated Pizza crusts,
babies in buggies threw rusks, and
over the twitching carpet of pigeons
pensioners shook out their last crumbs.
I stood there, wholemeal bread in hand,
watching the light on snow wings
as a flotilla of swans preened,
posed for camera phones.

Then ungainly out of water,
with flat black feet like wellies,
one raised her snake like neck
snatched the bread from my hand,
pierced me with her beady eye.
Left me one curved feather.

Christine Broe

Words turned to light
*(In memory of Warren O'Connell,
a founding member of Rathmines Writers)*

All books and papers archived,
the bookshelf stood forlorn,
we dispatched it off to Oxfam
in the hope of a new home.

Consternation when it reappeared
polished, laden with cut glass,
in Kilkenny Design's shop window,
only we knew of its past.

We kept a diary of its moods
as the window dresser sprayed
maroon first, amber, then yellow,
obligatory green for Patrick's Day.

We passed the news to one another
when it changed to a profound blue,
and finally a pearly white,
before it disappeared from view.

The Waterford glass it once displayed,
was bubble wrapped, taken home
to Texas, Vancouver and Adelaide,
Venice, Hong Kong, and Rome.

The crystal from Warren's old bookshelf
refracts rainbows the whole world wide,
so, now you too know the secret,
how words turned to light when he died.

Notes on Contributors

Margaret Boles

Margaret Boles has been with Rathmines Writers since 1996. Her poetry has been published in small press magazines and journals in Ireland, UK, North America and India. She and her husband have 5 grown up children and 4 grandchildren.

Christine Broe

Christine Broe, was winner of Brendan Kennelly/ Sunday Tribune Award 2001 and Premio Cittá di Olbia award in 2002. She has published two collections with Swan Press Solas Sólás 2003 and Lifting Light 2015. She has worked as an Artist, Art Therapist and creative writing workshop facilitator. Her web page is www.christinebroe.com

Eithne Cavanagh

Originally from Rathdrum, Co Wicklow, Eithne gets her inspiration mostly from the natural world. She is a founding member of RWW and her two poetry collections Bone and Petals and An Elegance of Gannets were published by Swan Press. Her poetry has been published in journals and anthologies in Ireland, England and USA.

Valerie Collins

Valerie Collins joined the RWW four years ago. She says "Every month I write an essay for the workshop and receive a genuine and generous feedback from the members present. I get a great buzz listening to everyone read." She works as a special needs assistant. She is married to Michael, they have five children.

James Conway

James Conway is founder of the RWW. He has been writing poetry and prose for over 30 years. Winner of the 2017 Jonathan Swift Prose Competition. His book Vertebrae of Journey was published by Swan Press in 2010. His second book, Purple Coat, was published by Lapwing press in 2018.

Philomena Conway

Philomena Conway, a native of Co. Tipperary, much missed Organiser and Co-ordinator of numerous projects for RWW most noteworthy the 2004 Festival & Writing Competition and the Open International Gatherings Festival, 2013. She attended Listowel Writers Festival many times. This is her only published poem.

Brendan Devlin

Brendan Devlin is a librarian and has been writing poetry for a number of years. He seeks to weave his interest in philosophy and nature into his work. He would consider most of his completed work as journey poems those which point to a destination not yet reached.

Stephen Dineen

Stephen Dineen grew up in Dublin. After studying history and politics, then travelling, he began a chequered career that has encompassed academia, politics, journalism and the civil service. He has had five short stories published and was long-listed for the 2012 Fish Short Story Competition. He lives in Dublin. In his spare time he runs.

Ruth Egan

Ruth Egan is an Irish poet originally from Limerick but now based in Dublin. She has had work published in poetry journals A New Ulster and Verbal Art, and in Baby BEEF Zine. She was also one of the winners of the Liberties Festival 2013 poetry competition in Dublin.

Brid Fitzpatrick

Brid Fitzpatrick was born in Mullingar, now lives in Dublin. She is a graduate of NUI Galway and UCD Her first collection Poem Drops was published by Swan Press 2018. Her book The Book of the Brown Calf Moo-Calf has been reissued by Swan press.

Susan Flynn

Susan Flynn a member of RWW since 2001. She was placed first in the Francis Ledwidge, (2001) and also in the National Museum of Ireland "Moylough Belt Shrine" (2009) competitions. She was overall winner of the Hanna Greally Literary National Award at the Siarscéal Festival in 2012. Her first book, "The Animal Woman" was published by Swan Press in 2007.

Michael Gavin

Michael Gavin has been involved with the RWW for over a decade. He says "I mainly write poetry but have dabbled in some prose over the last two years. I love the group as the quality of feedback is very high and is both challenging and positive. I am a disciple of the Dublin football team "Up the Dubs"

Shirley Gorby

Shirley Gorby has had poems published in The Irish Times, as part of New Irish Writing, and in Poetry Ireland Review. She lives in Dublin with her family.

Mary Guckian

Mary Guckian, a native of Leitrim, a writer, photographer and founding member of RWW. She has three collections published Perfume of the Soil (1999) The Road to Gowel (2000) and Walking on Snow(2010) with Swan Press. Her poems were the inspiration for A Life By Victor Feldman (2015). Her poem Bog Cotton was included in Washing Windows? Irish Women Write Poetry, a 40th birthday Anthology from Arlen Press.

Christine Hughes

Much to her surprise, Christine Hughes has rediscovered her early adolescent joy of creative writing, drawing upon such mundane but evocative experiences as cooking and commuting for inspiration. Her style may be more self-conscious and cautious than formerly but she hopes this is occasionally leavened with a sprinkling of mischief.

John Hyland
Born 1948, he has always been interested in drama, music and song. He has been a member of many choirs, currently The Tallaght Choral. In 2010 he co-produced a show called Hero's Walk. He has been a member of RWW for 7 years.

Marion Kerrigan
Marion is a native of Clooncarne, Bornacoola, Co. Leitrim and lives in Terenure, Dublin. She sings and plays the fiddle and guitar. These are her first poems to be published.

Fred Lalor
Fred has been a member of RWW for four years, but has been writing for many years. He has a vast collection of often humerous but always unique poems. Since joining the group he has read at Rathmines and Pearse st. Libraries and taken part in the Bloomsday celebrations in Sandymount. He is preparing his first collection.

Rose MacBride
Rose MacBride is a native of Co. Donegal and has a BA, majoring in journalism from Concordia University, Montreal, where her Novella "Placement" published by Lapwing, is set. She is working on a play about Countess Markievicz.

Gerry O'Donnell
Gerry O'Donnell has been a member of the RWW since 2014. He has won the Francis Browne Memorial Prize and was Joint-Winner of the Phizzfest Poetry Award. He was also shortlisted for the Fish Poetry Award and highly commended for Jonathan Swift and the Francis Ledwidge Award.

Tayo Odelade

Tayo Odelade is an Accountant, who has been writing for several years. She is treasurer of the group. She has previously published with Rathmines Writers' in 2012. She was born in Nigeria and now lives in Dublin.

Anne O'Neill

Anne is a visual artist, holistic practitioner and yoga teacher. She is fascinated by nature, human beings and our uniqueness as individuals. She loves being outdoors. Anne has a preference for connecting with people over technology. She occasionally dabbles in writing.

Dominic O'Neill

Dominic O'Neill is a longstanding member of the group. He writes pieces with a magical tinge. He has written a book; lived in a castle; had plays performed in UCD, and the Ilac Library; been on local radio; and had a short film in the Galway Film Festival.

Denise Ryan

In 2010 her poem Flowers of Humility was read at the Dublin Famine Commemoration and the twinned Batter Park, New York event where President Mary McAleese officiated. She has been shortlisted and runner-up for The Francis Ledwidge, and Jonathan Swift awards. Her debut collection, Of Silken Waters, was published in 2017, through Ara Pacis (Chicago, USA). You can check out her website www.deniseryan.ie

Rachael Stanley

Rachael Stanley's work has appeared in Writing4All Anthology Best of 2010, Misty Mountain Review Nepal, and most recently in issue 15 of The Blue Nib. A slightly revised version of the Poem Cat and Mouse which appears in this collection was published in A New Ulster in March 2017.

Ronan Stewart

Ronan Stewart lives and works in Dublin. He did his Masters degree in the University of Cambridge 2012, and has written articles for Astronomy Ireland and the County Council. He writes a blog https://ronanstewartservices.com/ where he has written on topics as wide as Islamic history and Brexit.

Margaret Thomas

Margaret Thomas works in poetry, prose and drama. She joined RWW in 2001. Since then she has been published in all their anthologies and she has read with them in libraries and on local radio. She took part in the writing and production of The Ten Commandments staged at Smock Alley.

Michael Thurlow

Michael Thurlow has been a member of the Rathmines Writers Workshop since 2003. Since then he has written and published short stories and poetry, and in 2015, he finally finished his book, a comic memoir, "The Marley Man", a humorous history of Cable TV in Ireland. He is currently working on another zany piece about why his lifetime was a good one to live through.

Paul Turner

Paul Turner has been a member of the RWW for 15 years, having been introduced to it by Peter Conway, late brother of James Conway. He has been published in Ireland's Own and previous writers' group anthologies. He has recently written mostly travel based material, though he admits to having the usual 'unborn' novel trapped inside him, which he is presently wrestling from the claws of his inner critic!

Elaine Beverly Tyrrell

Born June 1958 to a South Dublin family with a maritime heritage. She has B.A. in Economics, Politics and Psychology and Postgraduate Certificate in Management and Applications of Information Technology in Accounting from UCD. From DCU a Postgraduate Certificate in Innovation, Enterprise and Entrepreneurship, she also has a Toastmasters' International Certificate in Public Speaking.

Margaret Zheng

Margaret Zheng is from Cavan, living in Dublin. She was highly commended in the Francis Ledwidge Award and short listed in Excel Competition. Published in many anthologies, a long time member of RWW she helped produce "Prose On a Bed Of Rhyme", Swan Press 2011. She is working towards a first collection.

Books published by Swan Press

Extended Wings 1, 1993, RWW Anthology,
   edited by Rosemarie Rowley.
Extended Wings 2, 1994, RWW Anthology,
   edited by Rosemarie Rowley.
Extended Wings 3, 1995, RWW Anthology,
   edited Maureen Charlton and Brian Mac Guigan.
Quartet, 1995, Eithne Cavanagh, James Conway, Mary Guckian,
   Warren O'Connell.
Quintet, 1996, Christine Broe, Sinead McDevitt, Maura O'Grady,
   Mary Shine, Jeremy Young.
Duet for Two Dubs, 1997, Maureen Charlton, Warren O'Connell.
Extended Wings 4, 1998, RWW Anthology,
   edited by Marie Mac Sweeney.
Perfume of the Soil, Mary Guckian, 1999.
The Road to Gowel, Mary Guckian, 2000.
Fistful of Stories, 2001, RWW
   edited by Kate Davis.
Selected Poems 1988-2003, Patrick Boyle, 2003
Solas Sólás, Christine Broe, 2003.
Invincible Darner, Pat Carr, 2003.
Bone and Petal, Eithne Cavanagh, 2004.
Phoenix Fire, Kate Davis, 2004.
Extended Wings 5, 2004, RWW Anthology,
   edited by Christine Broe.
A Sea of Bluebells, 2006, Maura O'Grady.
The Animal Woman, Susan Flynn, 2007.
Encounters, 2008, Stories and Prose
   edited by Pauline Hall.
Vertebrae of Journey, James Conway, 2010.
Elegance of Gannets, Eithne Cavanagh, 2010.
Walking on Snow, Mary Guckian, 2010.
A Life, Victor Feldman, Mary Guckian, 2011.

Prose on a Bed of Rhyme, Rathmines Writers' Workshop,
    edited by Laurence Foster, 2012.
The Ghost Orchard, Tony Keating, 2014
Lifting Light, Christine Broe, 2015
A Sense of a Life, Mary Shine, 2017
Poem Drops, Brid Fitzpatrick, 2018
The Book of the Brown Calf Moo-Calf, Brid Fitzpatrick, 2018